Irish Toasts and Blessings

Pat Fairon *et al*

First published in 2019 by
Appletree Press Ltd
Roycroft House
164 Malone Road
Belfast BT9 5LL

Tel: +44 (0) 28 90 24 30 74
Fax: +44 (0) 28 90 24 67 56
E-mail: reception@appletree.ie
Web: www.appletree.ie

A member of Publishing Ireland

Photographs © as acknowledged on page 95
Introduction by Niall Ó Dubhthaigh

First published by Appletree Press in 1992 as *A Little Book of Irish Blessings* and in 1987 as *A Little Book of Irish Toasts*

A catalogue record for this book is available from the British Library.

Irish Toasts and Blessings

ISBN: 978 1 84758 178 5

Desk and Marketing Editor: Jean Brown
Copy-editor: Jim Black
Designer: Stuart Wilkinson
Production Manager: Paul McAvoy

9 8 7 6 5 4 3 2 1

AP3821

Sláinte!

'In my young days, when two or three men went in for a drink together, it was the custom for them to go into a back room – a snug. They never stood at the counter. Each of them would strike three hefty blows on the table and, in a flash, the barmaid would be in to see what they wanted. She would be ordered to bring them a half-pint of whiskey and, in due course, she would return with a jug and a glass. Should there be ten men in the company, they would still only have the one glass. The man who had ordered and paid for the drink would then stand up and hand a glass of whiskey to the man nearest to him, who would then say 'Here's health' (Seo do shláinte) to which the first man might answer, 'God grant you health' (Sláinte ó Dhia duit). That's the kind of toast they used to drink and it was always with a blow of the ash plant that they summoned the barman or barmaid.'

– Niall Ó Dubhthaigh

'May you know nothing but happiness'

A Toast for Happiness

May you be poor in misfortune,

Rich in blessings,

Slow to make enemies,

Quick to make friends.

But rich or poor, quick or slow,

May you know nothing but happiness

From this day forward.

Life's a Journey

May the face of every good news

And the back of every bad news

Be towards us.

'May the face of every good news... be towards us'

Harbour in Kinsale, Co. Cork

Saying Grace

Like the goodness of the five loaves and two fishes,
Which God divided among the five thousand men,
May the blessing of the King who so divided
Be upon our share of this common meal!

Parting Before a Journey

May the road rise to meet you

May the wind be always at your back

The sun shine warm upon your face

The rain fall soft upon your fields

And until we meet again

May God hold you in the hollow of His hand.

Inis Mór, Aran Islands

'May the roof above us never fall in...'

To Friendship

May the roof above us never fall in,
And may we friends gathered below
Never fall out.

Enough is Plenty

May you have food and raiment,

A soft pillow for your head,

May you be forty years in heaven

Before the devil knows you're dead!

Traditional farm cottage window

'Your health one and all...'

To Good Health

The health of all Ireland and of County Mayo,
And when that much is dead,
May we still be on the go;
From the County of Meath, the health of the hag,
Not of her but her drink is the reason we brag;
Your health one and all, from one wall to the other,
And, you outside there – speak up, brother!

Starting a Journey

May the strength of three be in your journey.

'The strength of three'

'Lift the latch on your door...

At Christmas and New Year

May peace and plenty be the first
To lift the latch on your door,
And happiness be guided to your home
By the candle of Christmas.

In the New Year, may your right hand always
Be stretched out in friendship and never in want.

To Ireland's Patron Saint

St Patrick was a gentleman
Who through strategy and stealth
Drove all the snakes from Ireland,
Here's a toasting to his health;
But not too many toastings
Lest you lose yourself and then
Forget the good St Patrick
And see all those snakes again.

Statue of Ireland's patron saint at Slieve Patrick, Co. Down

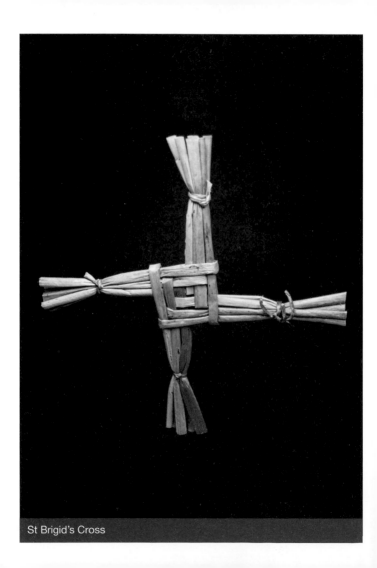

St Brigid's Cross

To Successful Fishing

May there be a fox on your fishing-hook

And a hare on your bait

And may you kill no fish

Until St Brigid's Day.

Sláinte!

The health of the salmon and of the trout
That swim back and forward near the Bull's Mouth;
Don't ask for saucepan, jug or mug,
Down the hatch – drink it up!

The health of the salmon to you,
A long life,
A full heart
And a wet mouth.

Ruins of a monk's fishing cottage, Cong.

'Here's to you and yours...'

To Good Friends

Here's to you and yours and to mine and ours.

And if mine and ours ever

come across you and yours,

I hope you and yours will do

as much for mine and ours

As mine and ours have done for you and yours!

On Going Home

May you have warm words on a cold evening,

A full moon on a dark night,

And the road downhill all the way to your door.

Interior of a 19th-century Irish Cottage

'Here's that we may always have...'

To All That We Want

Here's that we may always have

A clean shirt

A clean conscience

And a guinea in our pocket.

On Baking Day

Rye bread will do you good,
Barley bread will do you no harm,
Wheaten bread will sweeten your blood,
Oaten bread will strengthen your arm.

Traditional Fruit Soda Bread

'May you live to be a hundred years...'

To Growing Older

May you live to be a hundred years,
With one extra year to repent.

May I see you grey
And combing your children's hair.

May there be a generation of children
On the children of your children.

On Setting Out

Health and long life to you
The woman of your choice to you
A child every year to you
Land without rent to you
And may you die in Ireland.

Allihies, Ballydonegan Bay, Co. Cork

Harvest in the Mournes, Co. Down

Grace after Meals

Praise to the King of Plenty,

Praise every time to God,

A hundred praises and thanks to Jesus Christ,

For what we have eaten and shall eat.

On Good Intentions

May the grass grow long

On the road to hell

For want of use.

An abandoned boreen (bóithrín) or small unsurfaced country road

Irish Pub Window

Gratitude for Life's Blessings

May the Lord keep you in His hand
And never close His fist too tight on you.

On Hearing the Cock Crow

"May the light of the sun shine on us today," say we.

"The son of the virgin is safe," says the cock.

"Rise up, woman of the house and get the fire

going."

'Rise up, woman of the house...'

'Oh King of brightness and the sun...'

Asking for God's Help

O King of brightness and the sun
Who knows our worth,
Be with us every day,
Be with us every night,
Be with us every night and day,
Be with us every day and night.

Claddagh door knocker. The heart signifies love, the hands friendship and the crown loyalty.

A Greeting

Greeting: God greet you.

Reply: God and Mary greet you.

or

Reply: God, Mary and Patrick greet you.

A Greeting (in Gaelic)

: Dia duit.

: Dia's Muire duit.

Prayer on Milking a Cow

The blessings of Mary
And the blessing of God,
The blessings of the Sun
And the Moon in her road
Of the man in the East
And the man in the West,
And my blessings be with thee
And be thou blest.

'My blessings be with thee...'

Near Doolin, Co. Clare

Blessing the Cow

The blessing of God on you, cow,
And twice as many blessings on your calf.
Come, Mary, and sit,
Come, Brigid, and milk,
Come, Holy Michael Archangel
And bless the beef,
In the name of the Father, Son and Holy Spirit.

A Mother's Blessing

The great God between

Your two shoulder blades

To protect you in your going and returning,

The Son of the Virgin Mary

Be close to your heart,

And the perfect Holy Spirit

Be keeping an eye on you.

Shrine to St Brigid, Co. Kildare

Fishing boat in Howth, Co. Dublin

Going to Sea or Crossing a River

Going over the deep place,
O God of patience,
Take them by the hand
In case of a blow from a strong wave,
O Mary, look out for them
And don't leave them.

Grace before Meals

Bless us, O Lord,

Bless our food and drink,

You who has so dearly redeemed us

And saved us from evil,

As You have given us this share of food,

May You give us our share of the everlasting glory.

Baked Limerick Ham

Monasterboice, Co. Louth

Going Through a Graveyard

God greet you, all gathered here,
May God and Mary greet you.
As we are now so once were you,
As you are now so shall we be.
May all of us prosper under
The bright King of the world

For a Happy Death

When your eyes shall be closing
And your mouth be opening
And your senses be slipping away.
When your heart shall grow cold
And your limbs be old
God comfort you on that day.

Round tower, Glendalough, Co. Wicklow

Prayers for the Dead

God be good to their souls
God rest them
God rest their souls
God have mercy on them.

Taking Snuff at a Wake

Seven fills of Patrick's Island,
Seven fills of the tomb of Christ,
Of the blessings of the good God on your soul
And on the souls of the seven
generations before you.

Three Folds in my Garment

Three folds in my garment
Yet only one garment I bear
Three joints in a finger
Yet only one finger is there
Three leaves in a shamrock
Yet only one shamrock I wear
Frost, ice and snow
Yet these three are nothing but water
Three persons in God
Yet only one God is there.

'Three leaves in a shamrock...'

Drinking a Health

We will drink this drink

As Patrick would drink it,

Full of grace and spilling over,

Without fighting or quarrelling or hint of shame,

Or knowing that we will last until tomorrow.

We ask the help of our Mother Mary,

For she is our support at all times,

This is our toast to all here present

And may the Son of Grace be helping us.

'This is our toast to all here present...'

Water from St Patrick's Well, Clonmel, Co. Tipperary is said to have healing powers.

Good Health

'Here's health'
(Seo do shláinte)

'God grant you health'
(Sláinte ó Dhia duit).

Banking the Fire

I preserve this fire as Christ has preserved everyone.

Mary on the roof ridge, Brigid in the middle,

And the eight most powerful angels

in the City of Grace

Protect this house and this hearth

and safeguard its people.

Let us bank this fire in honour of Holy Patrick.

May our house not be burnet

or our people murdered,

And may the bright sun of tomorrow shine on us all,

At home or abroad.

'Protect this house and this hearth...'

'I make this bed tonight...'

On Making the Bed

I make this bed tonight,

In the name of the Father,

The Son and the Holy Spirit,

In the name of the night we were begot,

In the name of the day we were baptised,

In the name of each and every saint and apostle

That is in Heaven.

On Seeing the New Moon

On this saint's day which has
brought in this new moon,
as we are in good health at its coming,
may we be in good health when it goes
and when it comes again.

(said standing when one sees the new moon)

Ha'penny Bridge over the River Liffey, Dublin

Sunset over Donaghadee Harbour, Co. Down

At the Close of Day

I lie down with my dear God,
May my dear God lie with me,
The two hands of God about my waist.
A cross of angels over me
From head to sole,
Tonight and until a year from tonight,
And tonight itself.

A Blessing on Everyone

As plentiful as the grass that grows,

Or the sand on the shore,

Or the dew on the lea,

So the blessings of the King of Grace

On every soul that was, that is, or will be.

White Park Bay on the North Antrim Coast

Trinity College Library, Dublin

Before Work

May God bless the work.

Ending Work

The blessings of God on the souls of the dead,
And may the great God grant us life and health,
And may He prosper our work
And the work of Christians.

To Your Enemies' Enemies

Here's a health
To your enemies' enemies!

Here's health and prosperity,
To you and all your posterity,
And them that doesn't drink with sincerity,
That they may be damned for all eternity!

The Crown Bar, Belfast

Stained Glass in Maynooth Chapel

For Father and Mother

For my mother who raised me at her breast
And for my father who raised me
by the work of his bones;
I trust in the Son of God
when they enter his presence
That there will be a hundred thousand
welcomes for them
In the heavens of peace

Putting a Child to Sleep

May God bless you, child.
I put you under the protection of Mary and her Son,
Under the care of Brigid and her cloak,
And under the shelter of God tonight.

Lighting the Fire

I will light my fire today
In the presence of the holy, heavenly angels.
In the presence of Gabriel,
Most beautiful of form,
In the presence of Urial of all beauty,
Without hatred, without envy, without jealousy,
Without fear, without dread of
anything under the sun,
And with the Holy Son of God as my refuge.
Lord, kindle in my innermost heart
The ember of love
For my enemies, for my relatives, for my friends,
For the wise, for the foolish, for the wretched.

Peat (a traditional fuel) stack at Muckross House, Killarney

Carrick-a-Rede rope bridge, Co. Antrim

Going Out and About

The belt of Christ about me
On my going out and
On my coming in.

In the name of God who made a pathway of the
waves,
May He bring us safely home at the end of the day.

God be on your road every way you go.

The Emigrant's Prayer

Brigid that is in Faughart,
Blinne that is in Killeavey,
Bronagh that is in Ballinakill,
May you bring me back to Ireland.

Sails of the replica emigrant ship, *Jeanie Johnston*, Dublin

'Here's health and prosperity'

Acknowledgements

The publisher would like to thank the following for permission to reproduce work in copyright:

© istockphoto.com / Meredith Mullins (p4)
© istockphoto.com / Ramon Rodriguez (p7)
© istockphoto.com / John Woodworth (p8)
© istockphoto.com / Jonnie Morgan (p11)
© istockphoto.com / Donall O'Cleirigh (p12, 15, 32, 44 and 94)
© Stockpix (p16)
© istockphoto.com / rphotos (p19)
© istockphoto.com / Jack Lamour (p20)
© John Murphy (p23)
© istockphoto.com / Richard Goerg (p24)
© istockphoto.com / Meldayus (p27)
© istockphoto.com / Marie Cloke (p28)
© istockphoto.com / Ciaran Walsh (p31 and p73)
© istockphoto.com / www.hdconnelly.com (p35)
© istockphoto.com / Kurt Gordon (p36)
© istockphoto.com / Christopher Anderson (p39)
© istockphoto.com / David McFarland (p40)
© istockphoto.com / Linda Dalton (p43)
© istockphoto.com / David Shawley (p44)
© istockphoto.com / Mary Lee Woodward (p47)
© istockphoto.com / Andreas Kasper (p48)
© istockphoto.com / Gary Nash (p50)

Acknowledgements

© istockphoto.com / Manuela Weschke (p53)

© istockphoto.com / Steve Roche (p54)

© istockphoto.com / John Atherton (p57)

© istockphoto.com / Chris Schmidt (p58)

© istockphoto.com / Kelly Cline (p61)

© istockphoto.com / Rolf Weschke (p62)

© istockphoto.com / Brian Kelly (p64)

© istockphoto.com / Tom McNemar (p67)

© istockphoto.com / Patricia Hofmeester (p69)

© istockphoto.com / rognar (p70)

© istockphoto.com / Bohoe Photography (p74)

© istockphoto.com / Guy Sargent (p77)

© istockphoto.com / Graeme Purdy (p78)

© istockphoto.com / Robert Mayne (p81)

© istockphoto.com / www.BerndKlumpp.de (p82)

© Belfast Visitor and Convention Bureau (p85)

© istockphoto.com / Joe Houghton (p86)

© istockphoto.com / Nathan Gleave (p89)

© istockphoto.com / Nigel Carse (p90)

© istockphoto.com / Gabriela Insuratelu (p93)